Puppies Love

Thomas Trogdon

ISBN 978-1-7325552-2-8 (hardback edition)

First Edition
First Printing October 2018
Printed in PRC

Illustrated Photos, Design and Text by Thomas Trogdon

Created and Designed in the United States
Illustrated photos and text copyright © Trog's World LLC

Trog's Dogs™ is a trademark of Trog's World LLC

www.trogsdogs.com
www.trogsworld.com

A portion of proceeds from the sales of this book will be donated to Morris Animal Foundation's Golden Retriever Lifetime Study which is seeking to improve the health and well-being of dogs everywhere. To learn more, visit morrisanimalfoundation.org

Thank you for the love and inspiration **Shadow, Daisy, Paczki, ZuZu and Ginger**

For my Sweet Magnolia Belle

Puppies love running in the summer sun . . .

Do you like to play
in the long days of summer?

Puppies love playing with their toys . . .

Which of your toys
do you play with the most?

Puppies love to snuggle . . .

Who do you like
to snuggle with?

Puppies love giggles and grins . . .

What makes you
giggle and grin?

Puppies love rolling in the fallen leaves . . .

Do you like to
play in the leaves?

Puppies love giving sugar and kisses . . .

Would you like
kisses from a puppy?

Puppies love to be happy . . .

What makes you happy
and full of smiles?

Puppies love taking long naps . . .

When do you like
to take long naps?

Puppies love the winter snow . . .

Do you like to run
and play in the snow?

Puppies love hide and go seek . . .

Who do you like to play
hide and go seek with?

Puppies love days full of sunshine . . .

Do days full of
sunshine make you smile?

Puppies love time with family . . .

When do you spend
time with your family?

Puppies love to play fetch . . .

What games do
you like to play?

Puppies love smelling flowers . . .

Do you like to smell
the pretty flowers?

Puppies love chasing and running fast . . .

Do you like to chase
and run really fast ?

Puppies love sleeping at day's end . . .

When do you say
goodnight for bedtime?

Puppies are special and so are you!

Thank you for reading our puppy book